LAUDA SION
FELIX MENDELSSOHN

A Cantata for Soprano Solo, Chorus and Organ

A Performing Edition by Colin Hand

Kevin
Mayhew

We hope you enjoy the music in this book. Further copies are available
from your local music shop or Christian bookshop.

In case of difficulty, please contact the publisher direct by writing to:

The Sales Department
KEVIN MAYHEW LTD
Rattlesden
Bury St Edmunds
Suffolk
IP30 0SZ

Phone 01449 737978
Fax 01449 737834

Please ask for our complete catalogue of outstanding Church Music.

Duration: 25 minutes

First published in Great Britain in 1996 by Kevin Mayhew Ltd

© Copyright 1996 Kevin Mayhew Ltd

ISBN 0 86209 846 7
Catalogue No:1450059

0 1 2 3 4 5 6 7 8 9

Front Cover: *Heavenly Chorus* stained glass window at All Saints Church, Cambridge.
Designed by Edward Burne-Jones, produced by Morris & Co. (1865-1866).
Courtesy of Woodmansterne Picture Library. Reproduced by kind permission.
Cover design by Graham Johnstone and Veronica Ward.

Music Editor: Stephanie Hill
Music setting by Daniel Kelly

Printed and bound in Great Britain

Contents

		Page
1	Lauda, Sion, salvatorem	5
2	Laudis thema specialis	17
3	Sit laus plena	23
4	In hac mensa novi Regis	28
5	Docti sacris institutis	37
6	Caro cibus, sanguis potus	42
7	Sumit unus, sumunt mille	46
8	Bone pastor, panis vere	52

Foreword

Mendelssohn's cantata, *Lauda Sion* (Praise Jehovah) was composed to a text adapted from the writings of St. Thomas Aquinas and produced to celebrate the six hundredth anniversary of the institution of the Corpus Christi Festival in Liège in 1846. It was first heard on June 11th of that year in St. Martin's Church.

Unfortunately, the first performance was eclipsed by a wide range of other, more spectacular festivities – processions, fireworks and dancing – staged during the ensuing week, so that the work failed to make an initial impact on the audience of the day and, as a result, has been unaccountably neglected ever since.

This is sad on two counts. First, it is a product of Mendelssohn's mature years – 1846 also saw the completion of his oratorio *Elijah* – and it contains passages of outstanding beauty. Philip Radcliffe, in his treatise on the composer says that the cantata's 'spacious and polished technique deserves admiration.' He goes on to add that certain passages have harmonic breadth reminiscent of Beethoven, and that the final movement looks forward to certain Brahmsian qualities.

Secondly, the cantata's long neglect is regrettable in that the work is not too technically demanding and would be equally suitable for performance by both large and small choirs.

Lauda Sion is Mendelssohn's most extended setting of Latin words and its eight varied movements were scored for four soloists, choir and orchestra. In the present edition the original vocal parts have been retained throughout to which an organ accompaniment, based on the orchestral score and comfortably playable on either a large or small two-manual instrument, has been added.

It is desirable that a solo voice be used for the soprano passages in movements 3 and 6 but, for practical purposes, the sections for vocal quartet in movements 4, 7 and 8 could be sung by a semi-chorus or solo voices from within the choir.

COLIN HAND

LAUDA SION

Felix Mendelssohn (1809-1847)

Chorus
1 LAUDA, SION, SALVATOREM

Si - on, lau - da, Si - on, sal - va - to - rem, lau - da

Si - on, sal - va - to - rem, sal - va - to - rem, lau - da

lau - da, lau - da, Si - on, sal - va - to - rem, lau - da

Si - on, sal - va - to - rem, sal - va - to - rem, lau - da, Si - on,

du - cem et pa - sto - rem, in hym - nis et can - ti - cis,

du - cem et pa - sto - rem, lau - da, Si - on,

du - cem et pa - sto - rem, in hym - nis et can - ti - cis,

du - cem et pa - sto - rem, in hym - nis et can - ti - cis,

au - de. Lau - da, Si - on sal - va-

Quan -tum po -tes, tan - tum au - de, tan - tum, tan - tum

to - rem, lau - da, Si - on, sal - va - to - rem,

au - de, tan - tum, tan - tum au - de, quan -tum po - tes, tan - tum

to - rem, qui - a ma - jor om - ni

au - de, qui - a ma - jor om - ni lau - de, nec lau -

qui - a ma - jor om - ni lau - de, nec lau - da - re suf - fi -

au - de, qui - a

to - rem, lau - da du - cem et pa -

Si - on, lau - da du - cem et pa -

cis, lau - da du - cem et pa -

da - re suf - fi - cis, lau - da du - cem et pa -

sim.

sto - rem, in hym - nis et can - ti - cis, in

sto - rem, in hym - nis et can - ti - cis, in

sto - rem, in hym - nis et can - ti - cis, in hym - nis et

sto - rem, et pa - sto - rem,

sim.

hym - nis et can - ti - cis, in hym - nis et

hym - nis et can - ti - cis, in hym - nis et

can - ti - cis, et can - ti - cis, in hym - nis et

in hym - nis et can - ti - cis, in hym - nis et

can - ti - cis. Quan-tum po - tes, tan-tum

can - ti - cis. Quan-tum po - tes, tan - tum au -

can - ti - cis. Quan-tum po-tes, tan-tum au - de, tan-tum au -

can - ti - cis. Quan-tum po - tes, tan-tum au - de,

2 LAUDIS THEMA SPECIALIS

Soprano Solo and Chorus
3 SIT LAUS PLENA

no - ra, sit ju - cun - da, sit de - co - ra men - tis ju - bi - la - ti -

Sit laus ple - na, sit so - no - ra,

sit laus ple - na, sit so -

sit ju - cun - da, sit de - co - ra,

no - ra,

sit ju - cun - da, sit de -

men - tis ju - bi - la - ti - o, men - tis ju - bi - la - ti-

co - ra

4 IN HAC MENSA NOVI REGIS

in su - i me - mo - ri - am, in su - i me - mo - ri - am,

in su - i me - mo - ri - am, in su - i me - mo - ri - am,

in su - i me - mo - ri - am, in su - i me - mo - ri - am,

in su - i me - mo - ri - am, in su - i me - mo - ri - am,

fa - ci - en - dum hoc ex - pres - sit in su -

fa - ci - en - dum hoc ex - pres - sit in su -

fa - ci - en - dum hoc ex - pres - sit in su -

fa - ci - en - dum hoc ex - pres - sit in su -

ter - mi - nat. Ve - tu - sta - tem no - vi - tas, um - bram fu - gat
ter - mi - nat. Ve - tu - sta - tem no - vi - tas, um - bram fu - gat
ter - mi - nat. Ve - tu - sta - tem no - vi - tas, um - bram fu - gat
ter - mi - nat. Ve - tu - sta - tem no - vi - tas, um - bram fu - gat

ve - ri - tas, noc - tem lux e - li - mi - nat, noc - tem,
ve - ri - tas, noc - tem lux e - li - mi - nat, noc - tem,
ve - ri - tas, noc - tem lux e - li - mi - nat, noc - tem,
ve - ri - tas, noc - tem lux e - li - mi - nat, noc - tem,

noc - tem lux e - li - mi - nat, noc - tem,

noc - tem lux e - li - nat, noc - tem lux,

noc - tem lux e - li - mi - nat, noc - tem lux,

noc - tem lux e - li - mi - nat, noc - tem lux,

noc - tem lux e - li - mi - nat.

noc - tem lux e - li - mi - nat.

noc - tem lux e - li - mi - nat.

e - li - mi - nat.

5 DOCTI SACRIS INSTITUTIS

Doc - ti sa - cris in - sti - tu - tis, pa - nem, vi - num

in sa - lu - tis con - se - cra - mus hos - ti -

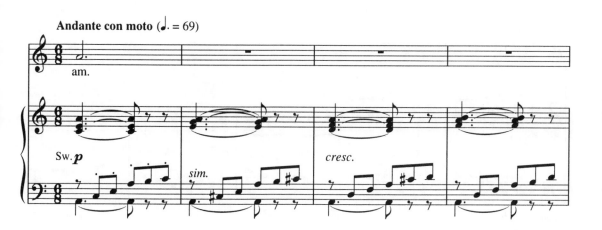

am.

Dog - ma da - tur chri - sti - a - nis, quod in car - nem tran - sit pa - nis, et vi - num in san - gui - nem.

tent,   la - tent,   res ex - i - mi -

6 CARO CIBUS, SANGUIS POTUS

tra - que spe - ci - e. Ca - ro ci - bus, san - guis po - tus: ma - net

cresc.

ta - men Chri - stus to - tus sub u - tra - que spe - ci - e, ma - net

mp

Chri - stus to - tus sub u - tra - que spe - ci - e. A su - men - te non con-

p

Ped.

cresc.

ci - sus, non con - frac - tus, non di - vi - sus: in - te - ger ac - ci - pi - tur,

in- te-ger ac-ci-pi - tur. Ca - ro ci - bus, san - guis

po - tus: ma-net ta- men Chri - stus to- tus sub u- tra - que spe-ci - e. A su-

men - te non con- ci - sus, non con- frac - tus, non di - vi - sus:

in- te-ger ac- ci- pi - tur, in- te-ger ac- ci- pi - tur; ma - net

ta -men sub u - tra -quespe-ci - e; ma - net ta -men Chri -stus to - tus sub u-

tra - que spe - e; ma - net sub u - tra - que spe -ci-

L.H.   *mp*   *p*

Ped.   Man.   Ped.

e.

rall.

L.H.

attacca

dis - par ex - i - tus.

Frac - to de-mum sa-cra-men - to, ne va-cil -les, sed me -

men - to tan-tum es - se sub frag - men - to, quan-tum to - to te - gi-

vi - ta bo - nis, vi - ta, vi - ta bo - nis.

vi - ta bo - nis, vi - ta, vi - ta bo - nis.

bo - nis, vi - ta, vi - ta bo - nis.

vi - ta bo - nis, vi - ta, vi - ta bo - nis.

Sw. or Ch. *pp*

16'

Andante maestoso (♩ = 88)

Solo *p*

Ec - ce pa - nis an - ge - lo - rum, fac - tus

Solo *p*

Sw. *p*

Ped. 16'

Solos

S A

ci - bus vi - a - to - rum:

T B

Chorus

S A

p

Ve - re

T B

p

50

ten - dus ca - ni - bus.

Quartet and Chorus

8 BONE PASTOR, PANIS VERE

Allegro non troppo ($\stackrel{.}{\downarrow}$ = 112)

Gt. 8'
Solo   *sempre legato*

Solos

**S
A**

Bo - ne pas - tor, pa - nis ve - re, Je - su,

**T
B**

Sw. 8'

Ped. 16' 8'

com - men - sa - les, co - he - re - des et so - da - les,

fac san - cto - rum ci - vi - um, fac san -

cto - rum ci - vi - um, fac san - cto - rum ci - vi -

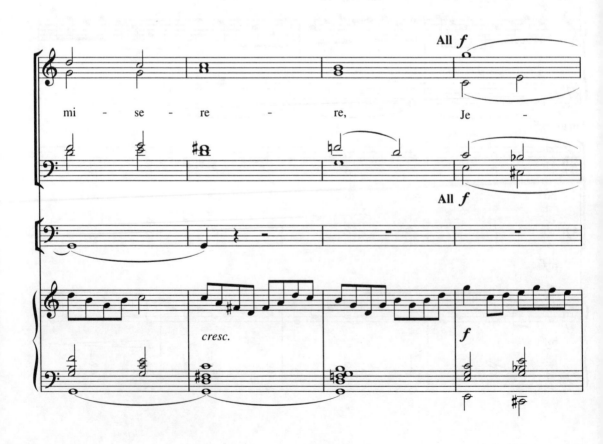

nis ve - re. Je - su,

nos - tri mi - se - re - re, mi - se - re -

tu nos bo - na fac vi - de - re in ter - ra

re, in ter - ra

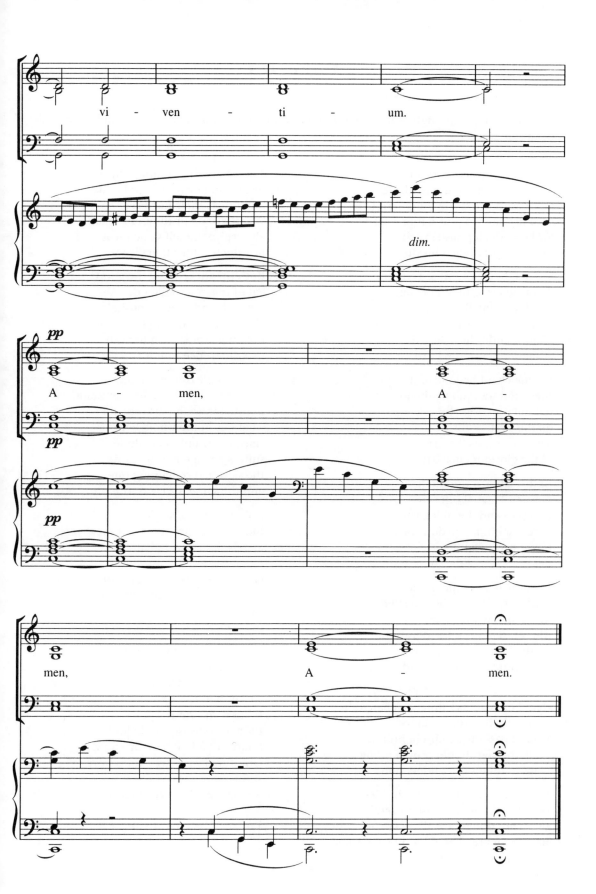

English Text

The following, although not a literal translation of the Latin text, is included to assist comprehension.

Sion, lift thy voice, and sing;
praise thy Saviour and thy King;
praise with hymns thy shepherd true:
dare thy most to praise him well;
for he doth all praise excel;
none can ever reach his due.

Special theme of praise is thine,
that true living bread divine,
that life-giving flesh adored,
which the brethren twelve received,
as most faithfully believed,
at the supper of the Lord.

Let the chant be loud and high;
sweet and tranquil be the joy
felt today in every breast;
on this Festival divine
which recounts the origin
of the glorious eucharist.

At this table of the King,
our new Paschal offering
brings to end the olden rite;
here, for empty shadows fled,
is reality instead;
here, instead of darkness, light.

His own act, at supper seated,
Christ ordained to be repeated,
in his memory divine;
wherefore now, with adoration,
we the host of our salvation
consecrate from bread and wine.

Hear what holy Church maintaineth,
that the bread its substance changeth
into flesh, the wine to blood.
Doth it pass thy comprehending?
faith, the law of sight transcending,
leaps to things not understood.

Here, in outward signs are hidden
priceless things, to sense forbidden;
signs, not things, are all we see; –
flesh from bread, and blood from wine,
yet is Christ, in either sign,
all entire, confessed to be.

They, too, who of him partake,
sever not, nor rend, nor break,
but entire, their Lord receive.
Whether one or thousands eat,
all receive the self-same meat,
nor the less for others leave.

Both the wicked and the good
eat of this celestial food;
but with ends how opposite!
Here 'tis life; and there 'tis death;
the same, yet issuing to each
in a difference infinite.

Nor a single doubt retain,
when they break the host in twain,
but that in each part remains
what was in the whole before;
since the simple sign alone
suffers change in state or form,
the signified remaining one
and the same for evermore.

Lo! upon the altar lies,
hidden deep from human eyes,
angels' bread from Paradise,
made the food of mortal man:
children's meat to dogs denied;
in old types foresignified;
in the manna from the skies,
in Isaac, and the Paschal Lamb.

Jesu, shepherd of the sheep!
thy true flock in safety keep.
Living Bread! Thy life supply;
strengthen us or else we die;
fill us with celestial grace;
thou, who feedest us below!
Source of all we have or know!
Grant that with thy saints above,
sitting at the feast of love,
we may see thee face to face.

EDWARD CASWALL (1814 - 1878)